If you have ever tried to make
things perfect and got in a panic
because it was all too hard,
then you will be happy to read about...

Text by Lois Rock
Copyright © 1996 Lion Publishing
Illustrations copyright © 1996 Roger Langton

Published by
Lion Publishing plc
Sandy Lane West, Oxford, England
ISBN 0 7459 3108 1

Albatross Books Pty Ltd
PO Box 320, Sutherland, NSW 2232, Australia
ISBN 0 7324 0968 3

First edition 1996
10 9 8 7 6 5 4 3 2 1 0

A catalogue record for this book
is available from the British Library

Printed and bound in Singapore

**This retelling is based on the stories
of Jesus' life in the Bible.**

Jesus
and the very
Busy Sister

Retold by Lois Rock
Illustrations by Roger Langton

A LION BOOK

Mary and Martha were two sisters.
They lived in a little house in a village.

One day, Jesus and his friends came to visit.

The two sisters were very pleased.
They wanted to do their best to
welcome Jesus.

'There are so many things I must do,"
aid Martha to herself.

"Jesus will be hot and dusty from walking here. I'll bring water so he can wash.

"And I'll make this corner of the room comfortable for him to sit and talk to all the people who want to see him.

"We've got lots to offer to drink...

and I'll make a big pot of soup and bake extra bread...

"Oh dear, will the fire ever burn and make the stove good and hot?"

Martha got in a panic at all she had to do. And then she saw her sister Mary: just sitting, just listening to Jesus.

Martha felt very cross indeed.

She marched over.

'Don't you care that my sister has left me to do all the work by myself?" she stormed at Jesus. "Tell her to come and help me."

"Martha," said Jesus. His voice was kind. "Dear Martha. You are worrying about so many things. But only one thing is needed. And Mary is already doing it.

"I've come to spend time with you, to tell you stories about God and help you understand how much God loves you. Come and listen to what I have to say.

"I'm not going to stop anyone who wants to listen to me. That's the very best thing to do."

A Christian prayer

Dear God,
If you only loved me
because of the busy things I do,
I'd have to be busy all the time.
But you love me because I'm me.
And you want me to sit
and listen to you.
Amen.